Singing in the Streets

POEMS
FOR
CHRISTMAS

Leonard Clark

London
Dennis Dobson

First published in Great Britain in 1972 by Dobson Books
Ltd, 80 Kensington Church Street, London W8 4BZ. Printed
by Chelsea Printing Services Ltd, 186 Campden Hill Road,
London W8.

ISBN 0 234 77635 8

CONTENTS

There is still a country character about the poems of Leonard Clark, though he is by no means of an age to look back into the world that was so natural and so unalterable to young people as into an eternal existence, which a reminiscent old creature like myself can enjoy without asking the permission of the critics. I do not know whether one should call *Singing in the Streets* poems of imagination or fancy, but the collection takes me back into an era and a community which Christmas especially dominated and made perfect — that was of course before the strange catastrophe of a great world war altered so many things.

"Christmas comes!   He comes,   He comes!" The urgency in that Victorian poem was one of the marvels of being a small boy as winter deepened and bells rang out more beautifully around one's home, or parish, in a peaceful land; Leonard Clark's poetry recalls such annual peace and joy. He was evidently from the beginning one who like Thomas Hardy would "notice such things" as precisely and memorably belonged to the solemn but joyful hours of the greatest things. I would be among the great number who thank and bless him for giving us the simplicities, the circumstances, the world-preserving qualities of high moments perceived by the very youngest as the bells rang out, how long ago!

EDMUND BLUNDEN

SINGING IN THE STREETS

I had almost forgotten the singing in the streets,
Snow piled up by the houses, drifting
Underneath the door into the warm room,
Firelight, lamplight, the little lame cat
Dreaming in soft sleep on the hearth, mother dozing,
Waiting for Christmas to come, the boys and me
Trudging over blanket fields waving lanterns to the sky.
I had almost forgotten the smell, the feel of it all,
The coming back home, with girls laughing like stars,
Their cheeks, holly berries, me kissing one,
Silent-tongued, soberly, by the long church wall;
Then back to the kitchen table, supper on the white cloth,
Cheese, bread, the home made wine,
Symbols of the night's joy, a holy feast.
And I wonder now, years gone, mother gone,
The boys and girls scattered, drifted away with the
Lamplight done, firelight over,   [snowflakes,
If the sounds of our singing in the streets are still there,
Those old tunes, still praising;
And now, a lifetime of Decembers away from it all,
A branch of remembering holly stabs my cheeks,
And I think it may be so;
Yes, I believe it may be so.

EVE OF CHRISTMAS

The frost has locked the stubbled land in chains,
Bound up the tongues of every meadow brook,
Blackened the buds, burst open trees and drains,
And given each curving field a hungry look.

The plovers wail around a broken plough
Fast cased in ice beyond the furrow's end,
The times are hard for homeless travellers now,
No beast or bird can find a hole or friend.

But soon a sparrow cheeps, and life wakes, too,
Where primroses look out with hopeful eyes,
And snug in swaddling leaves, the velvet shrew
Takes on the world for all his half-ounce size.

The stars are far and cold, the moon's blank face
Stares from the sky as if it were a tomb,
Making the earth below a sombre place,
Though life is moving in its winter womb.

On hillside slopes the ewes in littered pens
Brave blustering winds, first lambs are dropped,
And foxes lick their cubs in secret dens,
As if peace lay with them, and time had stopped.

And at this hour my heart is breathing warm,
The weather cannot bind my praising tongue,
The world for me is new and cruciform,
I sing the song that I have always sung.

JOURNEYS

I wandered over snowy hills
And down into trackless valleys
Where trees sang winter songs day and night.
I heard the seal at work in the ice,
The snuffling bear grubbing for roots by solid waterfalls,
The wind jangling like glass in the air.
And cradled in frost but warm as a bird
The Child lay at peace in the whiteness around;
A deer champed the moss.

In the deep, steaming forests I moved
Where the undergrowth trailed
Over snake-throbbing swamps,
And parakeets screamed in topaz and red
To five-coloured butterflies floating like breath.
And cradled in weed but cool as a rose
The Child lay at peace in the movement around;
A jaguar crouched at His feet.

I dragged myself over dry, empty wastes
Where death ruled alone,
Hooked vultures played on the last traveller's skull.
The sun burned my eyes to the brain,
Water, a mirage, poured into my ears.
And cradled in sand but new as a flower
The Child lay at peace in the desert around;
A beetle clicked under a stone.

9

I walked into the Bethlehem barn.
Its floors were of marble and gold,
The candles were lit in tall silver sticks,
The seats were of ivory,
The Book opened wide.
But there was no ox in the straw,
No shepherds, no sheep,
No Mother, no Child.

BELLS RINGING

I heard bells ringing
Suddenly all together, one wild, intricate figure,
A mixture of wonder and praise
Climbing the winter-winged air in December.
Norwich, Gloucester, Salisbury, combined with York
To shake Worcester and Paul's into the old discovery
Made frost-fresh again.
I heard these rocketing and wound-remembering chimes
Running their blessed counterpoint
Round the mazes of my mind,
Felt their message brimming over with love,
Watering my cold heart,
Until, as over all England hundreds of towers trembled
Beneath the force of Christmas rolling out,
I knew, as shepherds and magi knew,
That all sounds had been turned into one sound,
A single golden bell,
Repeating, as knees bowed, the name, EMMANUEL.

THE LION

He comes suddenly into peopled places,
A lion out of Judah,
With terrible visage and breath,
A voice like waterfalls.

He pierces with dread eye rocky places
And dark vegetation;
Scenting his prey he advances
To the world's edge and beyond it.

He roars hungrily in broken places,
A lion out of Judah,
Choosing lambs on green hillsides
Not to ravish but to woo them.

WINDS

The winds were talking together
In dead-of-night weather.

The North wind said,
>   I will give snow
>   To powder His cradle, bring a berry-glow
>   To His fledgling face;
>   I have no gold, no spice,
>   But can write His name in ice,
>   Winter in every place.

And the South wind,
>   I kiss those lips with summer breath
>   Carry the emblems of death,
>   Sponge, gall, tingling myrrh;
>   When forsaken in agony He cries,
>   Will waft Him home to Paradise,
>   Sweeten His sepulchre.

The East Wind said,
>   But what can I sing
>   At *this* child's christening?
>   I obey His commands
>   Long ago foretold,
>   To whistle a thorny song of the cold
>   Of pierced feet and hands.

And the West wind,
> Let me compose a roaring carol for Him
> To be sung by men and Cherubim,
> Send it around the earth
> So that everything in the tormented air
> Shall suddenly be at peace and declare
> The old news of His birth.

The winds were praising together
In prime-of-the-morning weather.

THE BIRTH

I heard the night turn over in sleep,
The thin moon yawn, the late stars creep
One by one from the freezing sky,
A clock start up, a baby cry.

I felt my heart turn over in joy,
I thought of the birth of that Bethlehem boy,
His mother, at peace with the breaking day,
Rocking the holy hours away.

I looked through the window pane to see
What grace had fallen, what mystery,
If shepherds and kings were waiting there,
If angels were dancing in burning air.

We knelt with the beasts on our quiet floor,
Knocked with our love on that stable door,
"Lord, we are here for Thee to bless" —
Our words turned over to thankfulness.

STABLE SCENE

We might imagine this Christmas night the stable scene
Mounted with all its trappings on a lawn outside
As if it were some familiar stage-set,
And we, behind our complacent screen,
Watching from the house in comfortable pride,
An amusing silhouette,
Mary, Joseph, Jesus, in their fixed places,
A trinity of cardboard faces.

No doubt we could plant the star above,
A piece of trickery in English air,
And with a surge of temporary faith and love,
Plaster with angels the amazed height,
Hurry the shepherds in before their cue,
Ring the Holy Family round with light,
Bring on the kings, complete the affair
By adding an ox, a lamb or two.

Do we know the story so well
We are no longer under its spell?

We could do all these, yet be no worshippers,
Only lookers-on at one of the old plays,
Following the incidents of that history
Though never discovering the mystery.
We should not hear how each frost-crystal stirs
And sparkles with desire to sing the night's praise,
Nor see the grasses tremble with peculiar power,
The firmament of stars tumble like acrobats,
The dead earth turn suddenly to one exulting flower,
Trees break into magnificats.

Yet, if our little son, aroused from sleep, were here,
He would not draw back if there before his eyes
He saw the very Bethelehem scene appear
With all the hosts of Paradise.
He would take up their sound,
Welcome the angels on his home ground,
Kneel with the shepherds and kings,
Heaven and earth in him perfectly reconciled.
So on this Christmas night we need no imaginings
To adore the Child.

THE BOYS

If, on this singing night,
We, at its starlit heart,
Could take our firstborn son,
His dreaming hands in ours,
Over each candled hill,
By fancy's roads and seas,
To fields near Bethlehem,
And that enraptured barn
Where every year for us
The winter mystery flowers again,
We know our child,
Not far from summer birth,
Would wake to Heaven's delight
And, unencumbered, recognise,
No changeling of earth
Or cherub new exiled,
But Jesus slumbering there;
And with the simple creatures share
The understanding of his infancy.
And we on grateful knees
Would feel the miracle and double joy,
As baby called to baby, boy to boy.
And Hers would have all Paradise at finger tips;
And ours a carol trembling on his milk-bruised lips.

CHRISTMAS ROSE

Midwinter, and the dead earth
Suddenly parts to give birth
To thick clusters of stiff flowers
Whiter than scattered pear tree showers,
Marble monuments or morning milk,
Smoother than pebbles or old silk.
I touch each blossom, where they lie
With polished leaves and golden eye,
The hellebore of the January snows,
The plant I call the Christmas rose.

THE ELEMENTS

Whatever you feel about them you cannot change
The elements of the season.
Of course, in the interests of history you can rearrange
Them to suit your purpose, find a convincing reason
For doubting their significance, dismiss the whole thing
As a sentimental legend for the gullible young.
You can do all these, and angels on the wing
Will not stop you, though devils continue to prime your
                                                    [tongue.
The simple elements of the season remain, and are these;
A stable, a star, shepherds coming in from the wild,
Joining with kings on worshipping knees
To adore a new-born child.
But a very special child though,
Delivered then, as now, into a world of greed and hate,
(For all the holly and the mistletoe),
Doomed to rejection, then to a murderer's fate;
There's evidence enough to prove *that* act
And the birth and the death still going on and on,
Reverberating through Time, a ceaseless cataract
Of praise and prayer. And the star, too, has shone;
As if what took place on that particular night
Had never stopped, still quivered and hummed in the air,
Still burned and glowed in the light.
So do I gather myself together at this hour, wonderfully
                                                    [aware
That the elements of the season are prepared again for me,
And for all, in their mystical company.

20

THE BEGINNING

Love,
Your love is my light,
Light on water, light in air,
Water and air my joy in You,
Joy in singing of bird, singing of star,
Bird, star, life and light to me,
Life in water, light in star.
You shall have my love all my life.
For what is now begun
Can never have an ending, will go on,
Love,
Flowing as water, air,
Rivers of Eden's joy,
To become the wine and bread
Beyond Gethsemane.
So shall all life and light
Fold back into each other,
Perfect, complete,
Be one again,
One,
As the holy beginning was,
Love.

AN OLD STORY

And is this the same night,
Again the same story,
Shepherds, a star's light,
Something about heaven's glory?

What is this night to me?
A tale mechanically told,
A dusty facsimile,
Myrrh, incense, gold
Resolved of their potency.

I have lost the wonder of it all,
I have lost the love of it all.
It was only a childhood fib;
Time has toppled over the crib.

But there is joy on my son's face,
Expectation in his eyes,
He sings about the place
Of Joseph, Mary, angels in the skies;
At carolling anchor, the three ships
Are riding now on his lips.

He is finding the wonder of it all,
He is finding the love of it all.
Even without the blessing of snow
He sees the mystery grow.

Like Nicodemus I have to be reborn,
Get down on my knees in prayer,
That I may stand with my son on Christmas morn,
Renew myself in his worshipping air.

That I may sit and listen to the same story
Told by his mother on the same night;
And all of us encircled by glory
At home, at peace, in the star's light.

PEACE, LIKE A LAMB

I lie sleepless in the half light,
Seeing through bare trees outside
The grey wolf sky of pallid stars.
I lie alone and wait,
Not for the tap of robin's beak upon the pane,
The unexpected wind that shakes
The icicles along the eaves
And ruffles up the new-dropped snow,
I wait for every earthly sound to die away;
Until from nothingness I slowly hear
Peace, like a lamb, move soft from field to field,
The crunching tread of strangers on the hills,
And unfamiliar voices in the trees,
And then, a waterfall of wings
Taking possession of the startled air.

THE RAIN

I heard the rain telling the trees
Of a sagging roof on which it once had poured,
Falling from the regions of a wandering star
Upon the hills and fires of hissing oak,
Where squatting shepherds saw through flame and smoke
Strange lights upon the soaking fields.
The rain told how it lashed a darkened world,
Smote three heaving camels' backs,
Folded sheep upon their knees,
The steaming, midnight ox.
And when its drops seeped through the rafters' cracks
They splashed upon the rutted floor,
And saw from all their flashing eyes,
Deep-bedded in the golden straw,
A Child asleep, all eyes on fire with love,
The stable lamp beside the creaking door,
And heard the heavens close and sigh above.

THE CHILDREN

I have their Alleluias at my heart,
And cannot restrain them
Breaking out to take their part
In the Alleluias of the New Jerusalem
With martyrs, archangels, Cherubim,
Saints, elders, and the Seraphim
Who continually praise Him.

There is no question of my not believing,
I have had all that out with myself before;
Even when blind to the truth, I was receiving
Signals and signs from some invisible shore,
Hearing, when most deaf, sounds I could not interpret,
And now, at this point in time, can never forget,

So that like these children, my faith, sufficiently strong,
Accepts what they can hear in this enraptured air,
The evidence of the firmament trembling into song;
Even beyond in space they see the heavens declare
The glory of God, and the sick and fearful earth
Waiting in hope the miracle of this Child's birth.

Let some of this blessing then pause over me,
I have more need of it than they
Who sense the Word, fresh and complete, in its simplicity;
Though I believe, I still must tread the way
To Bethlehem alone, that I may find the star
Shining above the place where they are.

I have their Alleluias at my heart,
And cannot restrain them
Breaking out to take their part
In the Alleluias of the New Jerusalem
With apostles, prophets, Seraphim,
Patriarchs, confessors, and Cherubim
Continually praising Him.

ON CHRISTMAS NIGHT

As deep I lay in dream on Christmas night
I saw a wonderful and lovely sight.

So rare and beautiful it was I must suppose
My eyes were looking at the veritable rose,

The rose of heaven Herself in splendour there,
Radiant with holiness beyond compare,

The never-fading rose of such vertu
She is untouched by cloudy Time's mildew,

Surrounded by a galaxy, seven stars on seven,
And blossoming on Her arm the Child of heaven.

"O perfect rose of all the world," I said,
"Your Child this night I have inherited

"To be the Prince of Peace for me and mine,
The living bread, the sacrificial wine."

"O new-born Child of earth and heaven," I cried,
"I see the doomed and broken man who died

"On Calvary's hill beneath a tortured sun,
And dying made with love, communion."

And as I watched, the Child and Mother turned
To where in fevered ecstasy I burned,

And looked at me, it seemed a lifetime long.
Then left me waking with an angel's song.

GRATITUDE

All night, beneath this roof of winter fire,
I lie, the dead hours at my back,
Waiting, as often in my childhood shire,
For light and life to come,
Christmas Eve to fade from the almanac.
And, on the edge of a dream, I remember how
Those old hours, slow and dumb,
Woke to the dancing of a star,
Snow fell sanctified on comfortable bough,
And Christmas Day began.
Yet, though I have wandered far,
A restless journeyman,
From those enraptured skies,
I am the same believing boy
Whose grateful heart and eyes,
Are ready still to wake in simple joy
To the breaking of life and light,
A morning of holy white.

OLD CHRISTMAS

Take down holly, mistletoe.
Do not burn. Put away
Glass stars, crib, until
Next Christmas Day
Brings the shepherds over the hill
With flying snow,
Shivering bird, berried bough.
But overhead the great star still
Burns clear in the holy sky;
Any minute now
The old stable door
Will creak open once again;
And then, by and by,
They will enter, those crowned men,
The white men, the blackamoor,
To fall down on bended knee,
Keep Epiphany.

NOTHING NEW

Surely there is nothing new to say
About this particular day,
Nothing to refurbish the story,
Give it a contemporary glory?
After all said and done
There is nothing new under the sun,
So why have it over again,
That business of angels and men?
Angels? What, still drag *them* in,
The evidence is rather thin;
That circumstance, too, in a stable?
Yes, a remarkable fable.
But why keep up the pretence
Of gold, myrrh and frankincense
In a sceptical world
No longer dew-pearled?

Christmas as now displayed,
Little more than a masquerade,
The season of counterfeit,
Kingdom come for the cheat.

Yet I cannot discard it all.
I am so bound to that Child in the stall
By a lifetime of carolling days,
My skies are always ablaze
When the winter star burns
And the season returns;
I believe that the air
Still quivers with prayer
As it did on that night
Of incredible light.

I cannot let my faith be put to rout,
My childhood's wonder wither into doubt;
I know there can be nothing new to say
But "Christ was born on Christmas Day".

SILENCE AWHILE

Be silent awhile.
            The Child is sleeping.
Gaze on Him now if you will for your own sake.
He is not long out of heaven.
            Angels are keeping
Watch over Him still.
            Do not wake.

Be silent awhile.
            Catch that frail singing.
Hear what you can now before for ever it goes.
            The whole earth is murmuring.
O, with what beauty that rare music flows.

That music? I once heard it clear.
            Saw the Child sleeping.
Dream or in vision?
            Now I cannot tell.
But He turned to me gently.
            And O, He was weeping,
They were my tears that started and fell.

I must listen again.
            Reach out for that singing.
Better rehearse my part now, it cannot be long;
Each moment that passes,
            I believe it is bringing
Me nearer the source of the singer and song.

Bathe in its beauty.
                    I came here with the singing
But heeded it not.
                    Now it has gone from the earth.
I pray that some vestiges still round me are clinging.
Sufficient to give me new sight, second birth.

So life nearly over,
                    I must be silent awhile.
Wait patiently now.
                    Let me gaze on that radiance once more,
That in His mercy all that is tarnished and vile
Fall from me.
                    I walk again clean on some other far shore.

FOR CHRISTMAS DAY

And is the wonder of the mystery lost,
The recognition of this day become
A point in time, a dimming Pentecost,
And all those angels suddenly struck dumb?

What does that birth at Bethlehem still mean?
A tale for children told by candlelight?
Where's evidence that there had ever been
The shepherds, and a new star in the night?

No welcome for Him, still unknown
To greedy eyes that will not wait to see
How treasures of the earth turn hearts to stone
And Calvary's cross into a Christmas tree.

And if no crumb of simple faith remains,
The manger and the tomb go tumbling down,
The Child submerged in fallen paper chains,
Each King deceived, and wears a tinsel crown.

Mock if you will, and arrogantly dismiss
The whole significance to be absurd,
Betray your gifts with one more Judas kiss,
Deny the truth, the essence of the Word.

I cannot cast a jot of it away,
I wait in silence for my heart to glow,
For private words my mumbling tongue can say,
The gift of peace, and tears of joy to flow.

I hear that wondrous music sounding still
In every particle of holy air,
I see the vault of Heaven begin to fill,
With all the saints and sinners praising there.

Such happiness and bliss, such inner sense
Of certainty, dispelling fears and doubt,
Is Heaven itself, and more than recompense,
Enough to put the hosts of Hell to rout.

THEN AND NOW

Then. A song of triumph at the night's turning.
Everything new again as on the first day,
Earth at one with heaven, men and angels,
Seraphim walking with shepherds on the hills,
Fish leaping to the stars, trees bowing,
Every stem tipped with life.
Winter fields flowered a few moments in eternity,
Wild and tame rejoiced together.

And all for a Child.

And now. A cry of gladness at the dawn's breaking.
Everyone happy again as on the seventh day.
Earth recreated, men at peace with each other,
The same mystery of angels watching over,
Love leaping to the stars, heads bowing,
Ear and eye tuned to perfect acceptance.
There could be a few moments of eternity
If quick and dead praised together.

And all for a Child.

EVERY VOICE

Break of day, in waving dream
I heard some fields whispering together,
grass blades bending beneath familiar skies;
it seemed every turf was trembling
with wordless praises.
Hunched hedges joined in the concord,
thorn thicket and bud murmuring,
trees, black and naked, scattered on hillsides
moved humming branches in a bleak wind,
the hills themselves, transported and shaking;
little earthquakes of adoration.
And soon, listening birds, fluffed in warm holes,
woke, with their chorus, hedgehog and shrew,
to snuffle carols of the damp mould:
every animal drowsy in stable and byre,
bellowing joy to jubilant stars;
the dead stirred in their graves,
birth and resurrection ruffling winding sheets,
the sun rising to a great crescendo.

Every voice was there,
my head full of the singing.

I cannot tell what mystery was sounding there,
at break of day, that rapturous morning:
I woke to its fading,
but knew, dead of winter, Love had been born again,
earth clamouring for unison with heaven.

A SONG FOR LODERS

When frost lies thick on Eggardon,
And every pool begins to freeze
From Muckleford to Nettlecombe,
And hills are hung with sparkling trees,
O, then, to Loders we must go
Before the world is drowned in snow.

> So, here, my dear, and there, my dear,
> The air is singing Love tonight,
> And you, my dear, and you, my dear,
> Are trudging home in winter light.

When mists fall low on Eggardon,
And morning reddens sea and sky,
From Vinney Cross to Powerstock
The flocks of silent starlings fly,
O, then, as evening breathes farewell,
We take the rutted road to Bell.

> So, up, my dear, and down, my dear,
> The house is bringing Love tonight,
> And you, my dear, and you, my dear,
> Are trudging home in winter white.

When stars shine clear on Eggardon,
And field and fold are hushed with sleep,
From Yondover to Askerswell
The lanterns burn for wandering sheep,
O, then, for us those lanterns burn,
And, one by one, we shall return.

So, swing, my dear, and chime, my dear,
The tower is ringing Love tonight,
And you, my dear, and you, my dear,
Are trudging home in winter bright.

NIGHT OF ST. SYLVESTER

Open all doors. Let malevolence out,
all sorrow and brokeness out, the New Year in;
wandering spirits who have no home,
will find protection here, the fire piled high.

This is my night, I share it with you,
its holiness and future divination,
I, who once wandered, starless, to no place,
found you waiting for me in innocence.

Open all doors to our love,
the night is passing with bells and tears;
you hold me in certainty
as now these last strange hours hang on.

Let our twin spirits travel abroad,
hover over all who, like us,
love and are loved,
and do not understand the mystery.

That we may merge with them
and blossom in what dust must surely be.

THE MANGER

The manger is here,
here at the heart of the home.
We wait in silence for the old miracle,
the Child to be born again,
as in the long ago days of my wondering childhood,
I waited for the same hallowed moment to come,
looking out on bare country meadows
through the starred window pane,
snow out-topping lanes and hedges,
trees caught in winter's stiff arms.
I believed it would happen,
was not deceived.

And believe now, with equal certainty,
for at any minute now,
the shepherds will come wildly dancing
over one of these hills in ecstasy
whooping their joy to the great star
burning in solitary splendour
over the roofs of this house.
And then, the three kings, riding majestically
down this sleeping street, the night at the turn,
knocking in courtesy upon our door,
entering perfumed and golden,
the long journey over.

We shall all be here for this worshipping,
families and friends, Joseph and Mary,
the small animals and birds,
cat and mouse in a brief armistice,
robin and starling waking in the garden
to the far sound of unending music,
the Company of Heaven still magnifying,
and bells tumbling with praise in hundreds of towers,
every one singing,
every grass blade and cold stone.

A vision of beauty
beyond the world's imagining,
centred for us in this place, and everywhere
now, at this magnetic hour,
a dream of eternity made real
for all who wait for the miracle,
and kneel in adoration,
here where the manger is,
the Child.